# An Integrated Art Education

# Smart 8

## Level ②

This book belongs to :

## An integrated art experience that will develop your children into global leaders!

Experiencing arts convergence activities will help your children develop into creative individuals who are academically well-adjusted, and capable of integrated thinking. They will develop appreciation for arts.

## This book is written for future leaders in a rapidly-changing society.

The greatest paintings and classical music of all time have been selected in this series. Focus and physical development can be enhanced through dances like Minuet, Waltz, Ballet, poems and stories. Cultural experiences can also be enhanced through creative and imaginative conversations with interesting and fun characters in the book.
Each theme begins with logical ordering of trains of thought will connect the integrated activities in mathematics, science, and history. This aims to bridge knowledge gaps in various fields for the children to explore the vast world of knowledge and grow into happy leaders.

Whole Learning through
Artful Activities...

# Smart 8 - An Integrated Art Experience

**1. It targets the whole child and addresses different modalities of learning while integrating core content into art education.**

- **Multiple Intelligence**

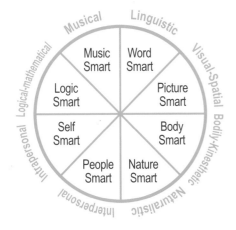

- **Whole Brain Development**

- **Healthy Habit of Body and Mind**

- **Motivation of Knowledge**

- **Communication Skill in School and Society**

- **Creative & Critical Thinking**

- **Appreciation of Artistic Wonder**

- **Comprehensive Musicianship**

**2. It buds diverse seeds of knowledge.**

**3. The music CD in the book will be a valuable gift.**

The CD will provide opportunities to interact and respond to art both visually and musically. With carefully selected music pieces, students are exposed to a variety of artistic expressions and given opportunities to develop their own artistic voice.

**4. Share the experience as a family.**

Sharing artistic experiences through music, art, poetry, and much more will provide a greater and stronger connection with your children. It will build character and provide a medium for bonding. It provides a guide for parents who are unsure of where to begin art education for children.

# The icons for integrated art activities

 **Poems & Storytelling**

having curiosity and interest in paintings

 **Think playground**

strengthening critical thinking, linguistic intelligence, and social skills

 **Music playground**

developing musicianship through classical music and relevant activities

 **Math playground**

fun and creative math with animal characters

 **Science playground**

little scientists' lab

 **Word playground**

finding connections between words and elements from paintings

 **History playground**

experiencing different periods and culture through art

 **Artist playground**

benchmarking world's great masters!

 **Global leader**

growing leadership and confidence

 **Let's create!**

improving drawing skills and imagination

 **Mission**

problem-solving

 **Dr. ART**

understanding art techniques and acquiring wonderful taste

# Contents

## CD List

| Music | Title | Composer | Musician | Story | Letter |
|---|---|---|---|---|---|
| 1 | **Bagatelle 'Für Elise'** | Beethoven | Subeen Choi | 7 | 8 |
| 2 | **Jazz Suite No. 2 - Waltz 2** | Shostakovich | Russian State Symphony Orchestra Conductor: Dmitry Yablonsky | 9 | 10 |
| 3 | **Romances sans paroles Op. 17 No. 3** | Fauré | Subeen Choi | 11 | |
| 4 | **Promenade** (Walking the Dog) | Gershwin | Saint Louis Symphony Orchestra, Conductor: Leonard Slatkin | 12 | 13 |
| 5 | **Ave Maria** | Gounod-Bach | Flute: Nora Shulman, Harp: Judy Loman | 14 | 15 |
| 6 | **December** (Christmas) | Tchaikovsky | Subeen Choi | 16 | 17 |

# 01

# Pianist and Checker Players

CD 1,7

• Henri Matisse •

Oil on canvas, 1924, National Gallery of Art, Washington D.C.

Mommy plays piano.
Brother plays checkers.
Home sweet home,
I love my home.

Flowers and stripes,
Red, black, and white,
Home sweet home,
I love my home.

On the wall, on the carpet,
pretty patterns
everywhere.
Home sweet home,
I love my home.

When I get my own room, I'll decorate it with bright patterns and cool pictures.
I'll fill my room with colors and music!
How about you? How do you want to decorate your room?

 Storytelling

⭐ Look at the painting on the left and talk.

💡 This room has patterns!
Which pattern do you like best?

💡 Does the room look warm or cold?

💡 Do you see violins?
The violins belong to Henri Matisse.
Where is he?

💡 What picture do you want to hang in your room?

Checkers is played on a checkerboard!

Don't you need pieces?

I want this in my room.

Ah~ Vincent van Gogh!

⭐ Teaching tips  Guide your students to talk about their living rooms. What do they have? What changes do they want to make? What do they like or dislike?

7

⭐ **Beethoven's Love**

Beethoven made this music piece for his love.
Listen and sing along.

"Draw a friend you like~"

El - i - se, I think of you to - night    I __ love you    I re-ally do    Lis-ten to me play the pi-a - no    I sing for you    a song of   love

⭐ **The most important melody is called the theme.** Make a heart ♡ when you hear this theme.

⭐ **Mimic Beethoven.**
He was a famous composer and a pianist.
He was a conductor and a teacher, too!

⭐ When you hear this music at home, remember to make a ♡ when you hear the theme.

⭐ Teaching tips    Sing the theme for your students. Show them that music they hear can be written as a score.

8

⭐ Listen to the music. Then create Beethoven and Elise's story for each part of the music.

When the main tune is repeated after the other tunes, we call it 'Rondo'.

Rondo comes from the word 'round'

 Play for me

Look at the rondo example below and tell the story.
Can you play the story on the piano?

⭐ Teaching tips    For further rondo pattern practice, students can create their own patterns using the template above to tell their story.

## Math playground

⭐ Place the stickers in order.   There are patterns just like in 'Für Elise'.

**Word playground**

⭐ Color the picture.

Let's play the piano.

⭐ Place the stickers below and trace the words. **Sticker**

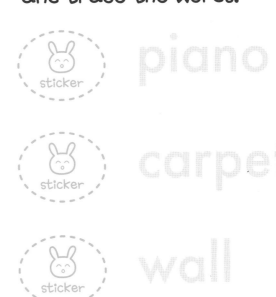

sticker    piano

sticker    carpet

sticker    wall

sticker    mom

sticker    music

11

## Artist playground

# Henri Matisse (I)  CD 8

### 1869-1954 An artist who loved patterns and the violin.

My Curious Friends,

I want to tell you how I became an artist.

When I was 21 years old, I was very sick ➕.

I stayed in the hospital for several months.

In the hospital, I met a very good painter.

I really envied him. Then one day, my mom 👩 got

me a book on art and paints  !

She said, "Matisse, you don't have to draw well,

do what your heart tells you!"

That's how I became an artist! Colorful patterns

make me happy. Do you want to try, too?

Henri Matisse

"Picasso is my good friend"

Matisse paints beautiful and elegant pictures.

Picasso          Matisse

Best Friends!

"I became an artist because I was in the hospital! Lucky me!"

12

# Interior design

Interior design is decorating with furniture, wallpaper, and accessories.
Matisse decorated his home with pictures and patterns.

★ Decorate your home with stickers and colors. **Sticker** **CD1**

★ **Teaching tips**   Help students draw patterns on the wall and decorate using different stickers. Students can draw things they want in the room.

13

# Patterns

**Matisse** loved making **patterns**.
Patterns are repeated designs. Everyone can make patterns.
Just draw repeated designs.

- From Matisse paintings -

"Music has patterns, too!"

One little Two little Three little patterns!

"Do you hear the pattern?"

PAM papa

PAM papa
PAM papa

★ Teaching tips    Let each student play their own rhythm pattern, and the rest of the students mimic.

**Let's create!**

Draw or use stickers to create your own pattern.

Henri Matisse "La Gerbe"

Henri Matisse "Polynesia, the Sea"

"Finished patterns!"

Play for me

Play your own music to match your patterns.

15

# Icarus

CD 2,9

• Henri Matisse •

Up, up, up. I want to touch the sky.
Higher and higher, I'm flying to the sky.

Up, up, up. I want to touch the sun.
Closer and closer, I'm flying to the sun.

Oh, no! I'm too close to the sun!
Down, down, down, I'm falling into the sea.

Cut-out, 1946, Centre Georges Pompidou

Icarus escapes from a deep cave.
He flies with the wings his father made.
"Icarus, fly away, but don't fly too high and too close to the sun. Your wings will melt."
Icarus starts to fly! He flies too close to the sun!
The feathers start to melt.
Icarus falls into the sea.

Storytelling

⭐ Look at the painting on the left and talk.

Imagine you have wings! What do you want to do?

Where do you want to go?
Who do you want to take?

Poor Icarus... so sad. Change the story to a happy ending!

What can fly in the sky?

 **Music playground**

CD2 Shostakovich *Jazz Suite No. 2 'Waltz 2'*

"Guess, who I am!"

⭐ Play the role of Icarus and tell the story.

⭐ Listen to the music and play with a balloon.

toss the balloon

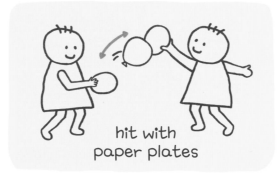

hit with paper plates

kick and pass

bounce on a scarf

blow to pass the ball

decorate the balloon

⭐ Follow the balloon conducting and play your instrument.
When the balloon is high, play your instrument loudly. When the balloon is low, play your instrument softly. When the balloon is gone, stop playing.

⭐ **Teaching tips** You can use balloons or scarves as wings when playing the role of Icarus. Playing with balloons develops a sense of rhythm and movement.

18

⭐ Waltz is a dance with 3 beats. Count ①-②-③, and stomp on beat ①.

⭐ You can also clap your hands! Stomp your foot on ①, clap-clap on ②-③.
'Stomp-clap-clap'

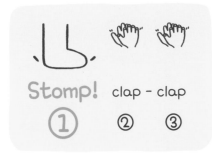

Stomp! clap – clap
① ② ③

Stomp! clap – clap
① ② ③

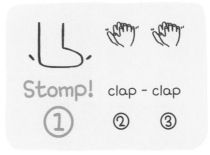

Stomp! clap – clap
① ② ③

Stomp! clap – clap
① ② ③

⭐ Try drumming on the table with your hands.

Left right – right
① ② ③

Left right – right
① ② ③

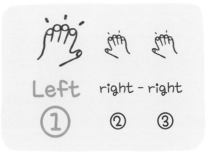

Left right – right
① ② ③

Left right – right
① ② ③

⭐ Teaching tips    Help students feel the rhythm of the waltz through walking activities rather than dancing. You can use instruments for the first of the 3 beats.
This is helpful for bimanual coordination in piano and understanding rhythm.

 **My Icarus** Mission

⭐ Place the stickers below to finish the puzzle. Sticker

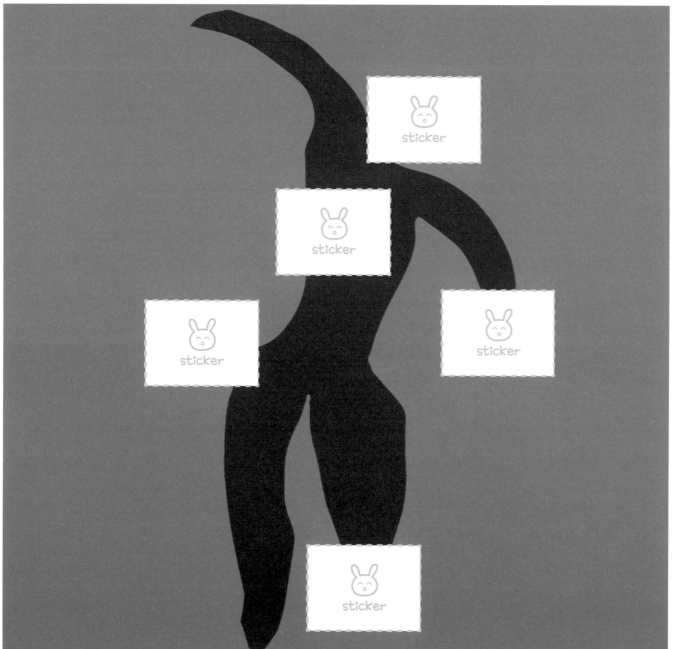

sticker

sticker

sticker

sticker

sticker

"Ta-da! My masterpiece!"

20

⭐ Color the picture.

 CD2

I want to fly!

⭐ Place the stickers below Sticker and trace the words.

 wing

 balloon

 elephant

 pig

 panda

21

# Henri Matisse(II)  CD 10

## 1869-1954 Artist who creates with scissors.

My Friends,

I am more than 70 years old. My doctor says

I have cancer. I am too weak to paint.

I lie in bed all day. I have a great idea!

I cut-out colored papers ◆◆ instead of

painting! I make a book with my cut-outs.

I name it JAZZ! It is improvised and has

rhythm just like jazz music.

Don't give up! You can always find a way.

Henri Matisse

Henri Matisse, The Funeral of Pierrot (from Jazz)

"Cut-out is fun!"

"Snip-snip, cut with scissors!"

## Science playground

# How do birds fly?

Birds are light. They have holes in their bones .
They have air pockets and muscles to move their wings.
They flap their wings. Air moves over
the wings and lifts the bird up into the air!

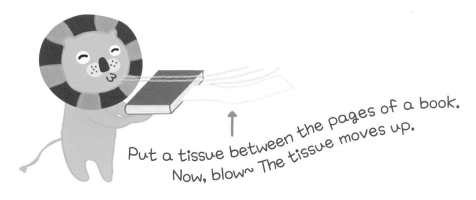

Put a tissue between the pages of a book.
Now, blow~ The tissue moves up.

★ Place the stickers below to help your
friend fly. Use a propeller
and a poop sticker! **Sticker**

"Planes need a propeller and an engine to fly!"

"I poop right away to keep light."

Oh~ No!

# Some birds cannot fly!

**Ostrich**

**Penguin**

**Kiwi bird**

Looks like a kiwi fruit!

The Kiwi is a symbol of New Zealand.

"...but I can run!"    "...but I can swim!"    "...but I can smell!"

23

# Cut-out

**Cut-out** is **cutting** paper and **pasting** it onto paper or canvas.
Matisse was famous for his cut-outs.
You can fold, tear, cut, and glue colored papers.
You can use magazines, leaves or pictures.
We call this a **collage**. It means to glue in French.

Fold and cut

Collage

★ This is a cut-out by Matisse. Can you guess what it is? **Sticker**

💡 It moves very slowly.

💡 It carries a shell on its back.

💡 The shell has a spiral 🌀 shape.

💡 It can live in water and on land.

It's a ( sticker ) !
Doesn't it look brave and happy!

"He made this at age 84!"

"I want to try, too!"

 **Let's create!**

**Make your own cut-out like 'The Snail'. Use the colored papers on page 69.**

 CD2

 ★ Teaching tips   You can create a collage using cut-outs from magazines or fold and cut colored papers.

Oil on canvas, 1872, Museum Marmottan

# Impression, Sunrise

• Claude Monet •

Hello, red sun!
You make the sky bright.
You fill the sea with light.

Hello, sea breeze!
You make the sea twinkle.
You make the sea wiggle.

Hello, boatman!
Are you going to the sea?
Take me there, please!

Do you see the painting? How do you feel? We call that feeling 'impression'.
What is your first impression? Are the colors soothing? Is the light warm?
At first people made fun of this painting because it didn't look real,
but it became one of the most loved paintings.

⭐ Look at the painting on the left and talk.

💡 What do you think are 3 beautiful things in this painting?

💡 Do you see the red color in the sea? Is the sea really red?

💡 What time of day is it? Is the sun going up or down? Is it windy?

💡 Find people rowing the boat! Where are they going?

27

⭐ Composer, **Gabriel Fauré**

Fauré and Monet both lived in **France** 🇫🇷 in the same period.
He was Debussy's teacher, an impressionist musician.

⭐ **Let's go on a boat!** Rock, rock, rock your boat~
Listen to the music and put your hand on the ground one at a time.

"Rock the boat to the rhythm."

"Row the boat to the melody."

⭐ **Let's go for a drive along the beach.** Choose your ride!

Feel the sea breeze! Zoooom!

⭐ Teaching tips   Guide your students to use their entire body to understand the sense of the 'rocking rhythm' and musical direction. Help them feel the macro beat. You can play with a paper boat or use a parachute as the boat.

⭐ **Enjoy a boat ride with a hula hoop.**

Create any motion to show the movement of the sea, the boat, the sun...

roll

rock, left and right

up, down

⭐ **Walk around the hula hoop. When the bell 🔔 rings, jump in and freeze.**

When the bell rings again, jump out and play again.

Ding!

⭐ Teaching tips    Help students play creatively with the hula hoop. The act of jumping inside the hoop teaches students to listen to phrases. This increases their concentration.

# Claude Monet

1840-1926  An impressionist who loved light.

"Monet loved..."

💙 changes in color and light

💙 gardens

💙 family

💙 water lilies

💙 his artist friends

Have some bread!

Thank you.

Pissarro    Manet    Monet

⭐ What do you like? Tell us things that you like and explain why you like them.

## Word playground

★ Color the picture.  CD3

Good Morning!

★ Place the stickers below and trace the words. Sticker

 sky

 ship

 boat

 sun

 sea

31

# Science playground

## Why does the **sun rise**  in the **morning**?

The **earth** goes around once a day. We call this rotation.

I don't move!

→

It is daytime for the countries that face the sun. ☀
It is nighttime for the countries that face the oppsite side. 🌙

Good morning!

Good night~

# The earth  goes around the sun!

The earth goes around the sun. We call this revolution.
It takes 1 year to go around the sun.
The earth is tilted as it revolves around the sun.
That's why we have spring, summer, fall, and winter!

⭐ Play The Sun & The Earth

- Cut out the Sun and the Earth(p.65). Choose your roles.
- The Sun stands in the center. Blazing and glowing~
- The Earth spins round and round, around the Sun, counter-clockwise.

⭐ **Play with Flashlight**

"Flashlight is the sun!"

"You can use a balloon as the earth!"

⭐ Which one goes around and spins? Choose and circle.

 sun

 earth

⭐ Teaching tips    Play the CD for this activity. The Earth can move around and spin to the rhythm of the music.

# Dr. ART

# Neighboring Colors and Opposite Colors (Complimentary Colors)

Look at the color wheel. What do they look like? A necklace?

The colors next to each other are **neighboring colors** ● ● ●. The colors opposite from each other are **opposite colors** ● ●.

**Monet** used opposite colors ● and ● in this painting.
Using opposite colors can make the painting look exciting.

★ Trace the lines and match the opposite colors.

"Opposite colors look great!"

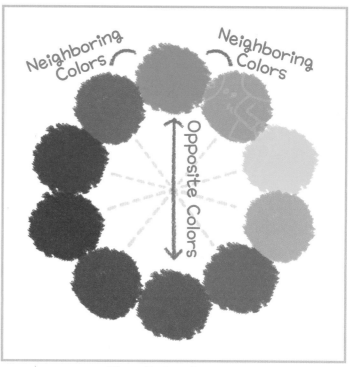

The Color Wheel

Let's create!

**Use the colors in Monet's Sunrise. Mix and match the clothes.** Sticker
Place the stickers below. Neighboring colors on the left. Opposite colors on the right.

Neighboring Colors

Opposite Colors

CD3

★ Teaching tips   Help students choose neighboring colors and opposite colors.

35

# Sky Blue

• Wassily Kandinsky •

Are you a bird?
Are you a fish?
Are you an alien from another planet?

Are you a horn?
Are you a harp?
Are you here from my dreams?

Are you in the sea?
Are you in the sky?
Are you here to be my friend?

Nina, my sweet wife! 👧💙
I give this painting to you, my love.
The blue sky looks like your lovely eyes.
The bright colors look like your kind heart.
I want to listen to music and paint pictures with you forever!

Storytelling

Kandinsky

Oil on canvas, 1940, Centre Georges Pompidou

04

Think playground

★ Look at the painting on the left and talk.

Where are they from?
What do they eat?
Can they understand my words?

Who is your favorite?
What games
do they play?

Let's play 'guess who?'
Describe one creature in the
painting to your partner.

Look! We're floating in the air!

Guess who it is?
It looks like a turtle
and has a pink body!

I know! It has a checker
board on its tail, right?

 **Music playground**  CD4 Gershwin 'Promenade(Walking the Dog)'

⭐ Name each friend. Guess how they move. Make motions for each card(p.67).

⭐ Look at the card and dance to the music!

①

Look and listen.

②

Make fun motions when the cards change.

③

When the music is soft, fly on the magic carpet.

④

Listen. They all disappear. Poof! Like magic!

⭐ Teaching tips   Show different cards to the sound of music. Make interesting motions for each picture card. This activity is good for active listening.

⭐ This music is 'Promenade: Walking the Dog'. Listen and follow.

🦴 The puppy dog walks

🦴 The father dog walks

🦴 Go on the swing

⭐ Look at the card and play a musical instrument (p.65).

*p*

*f*

⭐ Do 'Catch-a-bug' clap and count to the music:

One - TWO - three - FOUR

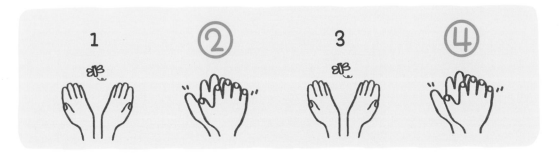

1    ②    3    ④

## Science playground

# My alien friends are not from here!

There are 8 planets in the solar system. The planets go around the sun.

Sun

Mercury

Venus

Earth

Mars

Jupiter

Saturn

Uranus

Neptune

"I want to be an astronomer"

⭐ Place the stickers below.  Sticker

- This planet is the biggest. It has stripes.          sticker

- This planet has rings.          sticker

- This planet is the second closest to the sun.          sticker

- This planet is my home.          sticker

⭐ Teaching tips   *The Planets* by Gustav Holst can be played.

# Wassily Kandinsky CD 13

1866-1944 An artist who loved music and shapes.

---

Dear Friends,

My mother 🙎 and father 🙍 play the piano.

I play and practice the piano 🎹 and cello 🎻, too.

I love music. I feel happiest when I play the piano 🎹.

When I was 30, I was a professor of law.

One day I saw Monet's painting and decided to become

an artist. I draw things that people cannot see,

like thoughts and feelings. This is called abstract art.

Look at the picture on the right.

Can you hear the song of circles ⃝ and squares ☐?

Wassily Kandinsky

"Paint a picture with ⃝ and ☐!"

Wassily Kandinsky, Color study: Squares with Concentric Circles

"Kandinsky loved this painting by Monet!"

wow~

41

**Word playground**

⭐ Read the shapes and color.

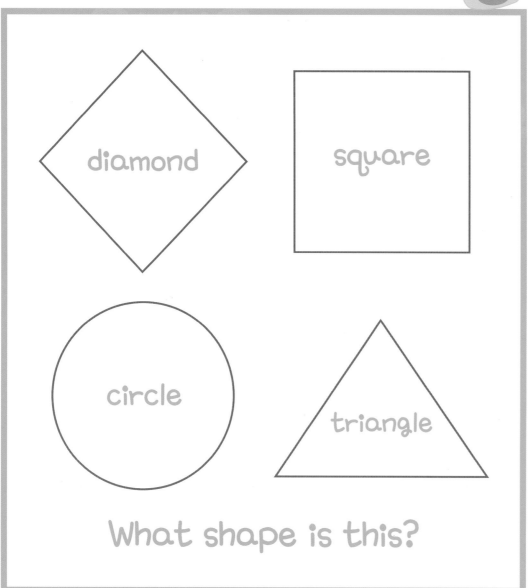

diamond

square

circle

triangle

What shape is this?

⭐ Place the stickers below  and trace the words.

 shape

circle

 square

 triangle

 diamond

42

⭐ The shapes are folded in half. Find and circle the complete shape.

1.

2.

3.

4.

43

# Abstract Painting

**Kandinsky** is the father of abstract art.

**Abstract painting** looks very different from real things.

It is a painting of things in your mind, like your thoughts and feelings. For example, Kandinsky wanted to paint **sound**.

He used **lines** and **shapes** instead of **musical notes** ♪. He composed with many shapes.

Wassily Kandinsky, Composition VIII

"Find ○, △, and □!"

 Play for me

**Play the sound each shape makes.**

 **Let's create!**

# Draw with shapes like Kandinsky.
What can you draw with a circle and a triangle?

CD4

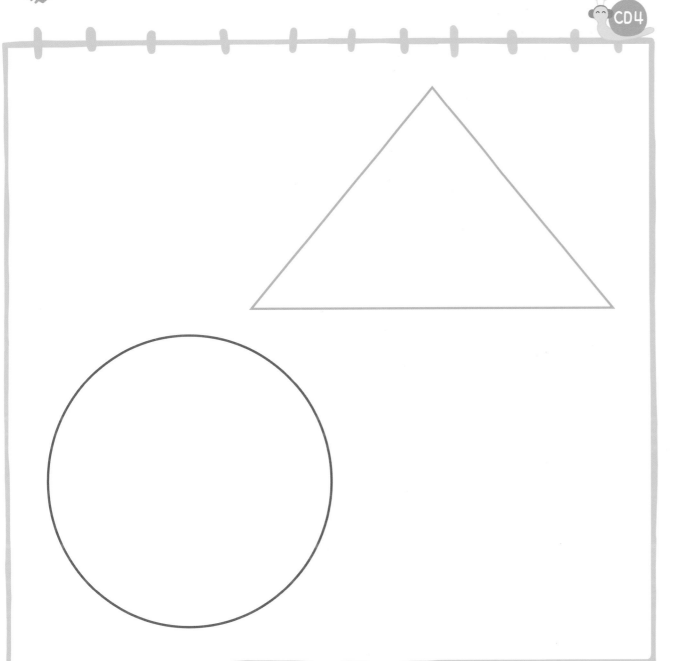

45

# Pieta

CD 5, 14

• Michelangelo Buonarroti •

Mommy loves me.
She prays for me.
She cries for me.
She hugs and kisses me.

Mommy loves me.
Her love is ocean deep.
Her love is sky high.
Her love is brighter than
the stars in the night sky.

One day, Michelangelo heard a voice. The voice came from a huge marble in a store. It was the voice of Jesus! "How much is this marble?" he asked to the owner. "Take it. It's too big to keep." said the owner.
Michelangelo made a sculpture with this marble. Later, this sculpture became famous around the world!

Storytelling

Marble, 1499, St. Peter's Basilica

05

⭐ Look at the sculpture on the left and talk.

💡 Count your blessings everyday.
What are you thankful for?

💡 What can you do for your parents?
What makes you happy?

💡 In some countries, there are children who do not have clean water or enough food to eat.
How can you help them?

  **Music playground**   CD5  Gounod-Bach 'Ave Maria'

⭐ **Slow and soft music relaxes me.**
Listen and mimic the sound of the harp and the flute.

⭐ **Take a deep breath and stretch your body.**

tree pose~

⭐ **It's fun to stretch with a friend!**

⭐ Teaching tips   Gounod added the melody in Bach's Prelude. The harp part is by Bach, and the flute part is by Gounod. This piece is great to experience a long phrase using big motions. Feel free to make simple yoga poses. You can have a contest, e.g., who can stand the longest on one foot.

⭐ Place the butterfly sticker on your fingernail.
Dance like a butterfly to the sound of the flute. **Sticker**

fly~

sit~

Where to next?

You can use finger cymbals 🔔🔔 instead!

⭐ Pretend you are a parent. What can you do for your baby? Move to the music.

brush baby's hair

rock baby to sleep

give baby a bath

⭐ Play with the ball like a rhythmic gymnast.
Dance and pass the ball to the music.

⭐ Teaching tips   Demonstrate using a ball. Help students feel the smooth connection between the melody line and the phrase. You can play the melody of the flute.

# Help me find Mom and Dad

⭐ Mom, Dad! Where are you? Help our friends find the way.

# Word playground

★ Color the picture.  CD5

Love each other!

★ Place the stickers below and trace the words. **Sticker**

 St. Mary

 mother

 Jesus

 son

 love

# Michelangelo Buonarroti  CD 15

1475-1564  An artist, a sculptor, and a poet
who knew the human body like a doctor.

Hello!

Are you curious about the human body?

Artists and sculptors study the human

body, just like doctors.

Look at the Pieta carefully!

The bones and muscles look almost real, right?

It's wonderful to blow life into a stone.

When people are moved, I feel great, too.

Michelangelo Buonarroti

"Somebody broke the Pieta into million pieces!"

"What happened to the Pieta then?"

# Restoration (bringing back to the original)

How did the Pieta sculpture become new again?
Restorers found each piece and made new pieces, then put it back together again. We call this restoration.
Sometimes paintings are burnt, **wet**, dirty or the colors have changed over time.
Like doctors who help people, restorers help repair and clean paintings, sculptures, and other pieces of art.

Before

After

### Raffaello Sanzio 'The Madonna of the Meadow'

500 years ago, this painting was broken into 17 pieces.
50 specialists worked hard for 10 years.
They used x-rays and other machinery to restore it.
The power of science is amazing!

"It's new and clean again!"

53

# Ceiling Painting

**Ceiling painting** is **painting** on the **ceiling** of a church or a palace.

Sistine Chapel ceiling, 《Book of Genesis》

You can do it!

"I needed a very tall ladder, so I invented one myself. Artist, sculptor, AND inventor!"

**Michelangelo** Buonarroti 'Book of Genesis'

The ceiling of the Sistine Chapel is very, very high.
It is too hard to look up and paint all day.
No one wanted to paint it. Everyone ran away.
Only Michelangelo stayed.
He slept and ate only little. His neck, back, and eyes hurt.
He gave up his health to paint.
After a hundred years, it is still one of the best paintings!

Let's create!

Let's paint the ceiling.
What do you want to draw? Use stickers!

My friends will be so surprised!

CD5

55

Oil on canvas, 1872, Musee D'Orsay

# Chestnut Trees

• Camille Pissarro •  CD 6, 16

Crunch, crunch, white snow.
Mommy holds my hand.
I am warm and happy.

Red house, red scarf and hat.
Yellow light in the sky.
I am warm and happy.

Chestnut tree, see you soon.
I want hot chocolate.
Hmmm, I am warm and happy!

"Van Gogh loved this piece!"

Pissarro's house is red. The little girl's scarf is red.
The evening sky is yellow. Red and yellow are warm colors.
Blue is a cold color. Cold blue on the snow makes me shiver. Brrrrrrrrr~

 Storytelling

# 06

Think playground

⭐ What comes to your mind when I say "winter"? Here's a Mind Map to help you think!

Hospital

Coke

2. 14
(Valentine's Day)

coat

amusement park

choco

cotton candy

winter

snow

white

I'm sleepy.

⭐ Body Language: Choose a picture and act it out. Play a guessing game!

Play for me

Play music to your favorite picture.

★ **Make motions for winter activities.** You can use an ankle bell.

go skating  +  jump & spin

roll a snowball     snowball fighting

climb down the chimney

go sledding

give presents

run home

★ **Connect pictures to the music.** You can see many repetitions.

★ **Teaching tips**   The patterns above help students experience musical structure. Change the motion according to the story students want.

**Word playground**

⭐ Color the picture.  CD6

My house is red.

⭐ Place the stickers below **Sticker** and trace the words.

 house

 coat

 snow

 snowman

 boots

59

# Camille Pissarro CD 17

## 1830-1903 The Father of Impressionism.

Dear Friends,

My dad  doesn't want me to be an artist.

He told my teacher to stop me from painting.

Because of my dad, I work at a shop. But every

chance I get, I go to the beach to paint!

There I meet my friends. They teach me how to paint

the lights beautifully. Now, I am finally an artist!

If you really wish for something, it will come true.

Camille Pissarro

"Everything is beautiful, all that matters is to be able to interpret."

- Pissarro -

Big brother, We love you!

"I'm the oldest of the impressionists!"

Gauguin    Cezanne

60

# The **tree** changes color every season.

⭐ Place the stickers below.  Sticker

(sticker) spring

(sticker) summer

(sticker) fall

(sticker) winter

##  Why do **leaves** change color?

The leaves in the spring and summer have red and yellow colors, too.
But the green color is so strong that we can only see the green color!
In the fall and winter, the green color disappears and we can see red and yellow.

##  Why do **leaves** fall?

In the cold winter, bears hibernate to save energy.
Trees also need to save energy and not freeze, so they shed their leaves.

 "I'll keep you warm~"

61

 **Dr. ART**

# Warm colors vs Cold colors

 **hot cold**

What color is the hot water handle? What about the cold water handle?

Colors have **warm** and **cold** feelings. Isn't that amazing?

Paintings have **warm** and **cold** feelings, too.

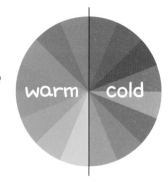

⭐ **Place the stickers below.** Sticker

Henri Matisse
'Red Room'

sticker

Henri Matisse
'Blue Nude'

sticker

Nice and warm~

 **Let's create!**

Place warm or cold color stickers below.  Sticker

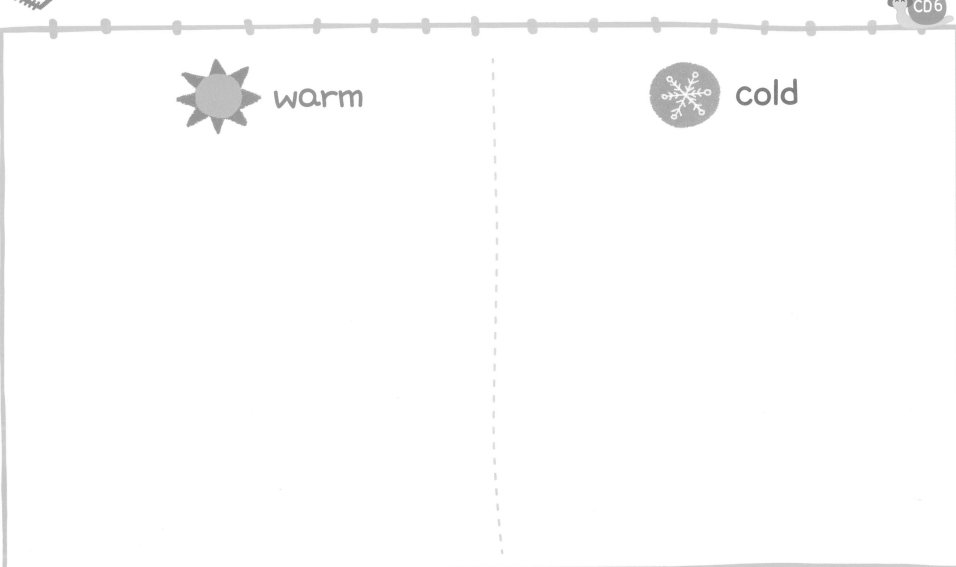

warm

cold

 Play for me

Look at the warm colors and play your music.
Do the same with cold colors.

# Artist Achievement Award

Name: _____

**This certifies that the student has successfully completed Smart 8 Level 2.**

**You may advance to Level 3!**

Date: _____    Teacher: _____

*f*

*p*

sun

$f$ forte

earth

$p$ piano

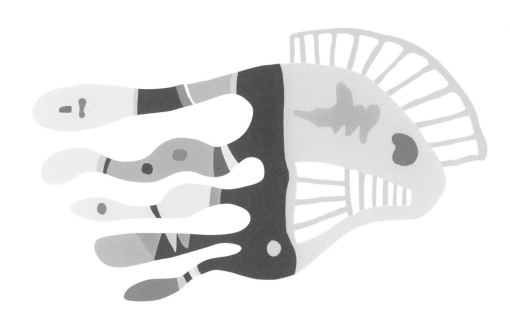

Name the creature.

Name the creature.

_____

_____

Fly on the
magic carpet!

Name the creature.

_____

p.10 Choose the correct stickers. p.11 p.13 p.21

p.20

p.23

p.24
p.31

p.35

opposite color

neighboring color ←→ neighboring color

p.40

Earth    Venus    Saturn    Jupiter

42쪽

p.49

p.51

p.59

p.61

p.62

heart stickers

winter    spring    summer    fall

p.63

painting stickers

# character stickers

# star stickers

# compliment stickers

 Very Good!   Good Job!   Perfect!   참 잘했어요!   Great!   Excellent!   Great! Great! Great!

 Very Good!   Good Job!   Perfect!   참 잘했어요!   Great!   Excellent!  최고야! 최고야! 최고야!

 Very Good!   Good Job!   Perfect!   참 잘했어요!   Great!   Excellent!  역시 멋져! 역시 멋져! 역시 멋져!

Great Great Great

Perfect Perfect Perfect